Maw's Saturday Kitchen

On Saturday Maw lets the family make their own breakfast.
They communicate by smoke signals and sometimes the police are called.

The Broons

Since first meeting Scotland's happiest family in 1936, Maw has had the difficult task of keeping ten hungry Broons full with her tasty treats. Whether they're gathered around the table with a roast dinner, witnessing Daphne's latest daft diet, or enjoying a fish supper on a walk home, food has played a central role in many of the Broons' brilliant antics. It is Maw's joy to keep her family well fed, although they can sometimes be hard to please. But, with their terrible culinary skills, it's just as well Maw's a star baker!

Oor Wullie

Oor Wullie has had many laughs with food over the years, giving him the chance to play plenty of pranks on the people of Auchenshoogle, as well as the golden opportunity to try and earn a quick buck. But after a busy day of causing mischief, Wullie loves nothing more than running home to a plate full of mince 'n' tatties wi' peas. His Ma's home cooking is his favourite, and he can eat bread 'n' butter pudding, jeely pieces, and jam roly poly until his black dungarees begin to strain.

Published by DC Thomson Annuals Ltd in 2016. DC Thomson Annuals Ltd, 185 Fleet Street, London EC4A 2HS

See Paw's face drop—

When the toaster goes " Pop "!

If To Be Wull's Pal's Your Intention
A Vacuum-Cleaner Dinna Mention.

Breakfast in bed . . .

. . . goes tae Paw's head!

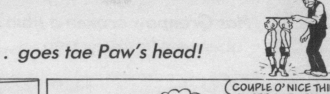

No wonder Paw's grumpy—

His porridge is lumpy!

These four scroungers think it's awfy—

No' tae get their cup o' coffee!

This ancient Scots method of preserving porridge suits Granpaw Broon very well. He stores it in the drawer of his allotment shed. When his old cronies come around they have a slice each which makes them very happy – none of them have their own teeth and sliced porridge is just the ticket. Maw suspects that the happiness comes from them washing it down with Granpaw's homemade tattie wine.

Jings, it's true! What a to-do!

The Bairn knows her onions too!

GRANPAW KENS JUST WHAT THEY NEED . . .

YE'D NEVER CALL HIM TURNIP HEID!

The Broons have had enough . . .

. . . o' that back-breakin' stuff!

MICHTY ME! THEIR GRUB HAS GONE!

THE PLATES ARE CLEAN, WHAT'S GOIN' ON?

They've a' got plenty to say . . .

. . . aboot the soup o' the day!

When you've soup tae sup—

Keep your moustache up!

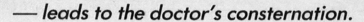

Paw Broon's piece-box operation —

— leads to the doctor's consternation.

Daphne is always on a diet and this is her answer – she only takes one sandwich per day. The weight is not exactly falling off her. Daphne thinks she will use less lettuce.

It's nae use lookin' —

— for Maw's home cookin'!

Help ma boab! They're in a tizz!

Does Paw no'ken what day it is?

The Broons Wish You All
As Merry A Christmas As They Got!

THE PUIR SOWELS THINK THEY'VE HAD ENOUGH O' EATIN' A' THAT TURKEY STUFF!

Has Granpaw broken a tibia?

Let's see if it's a fib-ia!

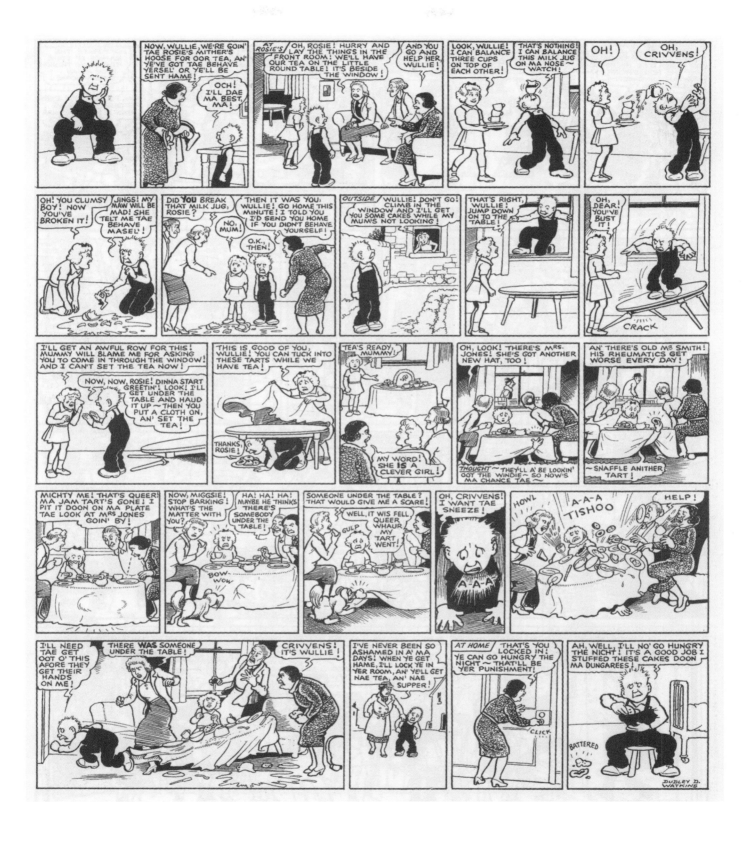

AND FOR ITS DENNER, THIS HIELAN' COO

LIKES CRUMBLE AN' A STOCKING OR TWO!

You'll no' believe the Broons' new dish—

The family's eating " flying " fish!

See Paw "carry oot" his plan—

Then keep a straight face if ye can!

Hen says he fell in love with Italian cuisine on a holiday to Rome, although nobody remembers him ever going further than the Isle of Skye. The family think it's the fact that spaghetti is long and thin – just like him.

Oor Wullie Made A Splendid Waiter,

But Got The " Tip " From His Mother Later.

An expert cook?—

Well, tak' a look!

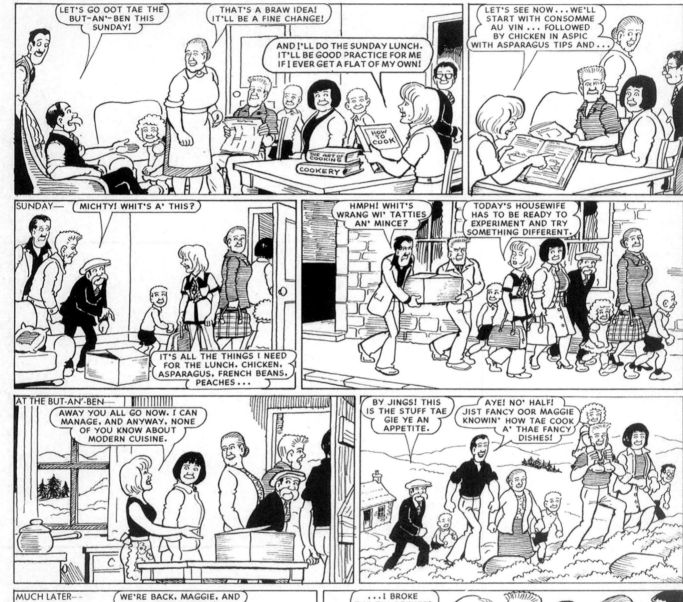

There micht no' be turkey for Christmas dinner —

— but Paw Broon thinks he's onto a winner!

Daph's lad cannae believe his eyes —

— at the results o' her diet an' exercise.

Wullie Managed To Mind The Bairn,

But In Mindin' The Rest He Wasna Spairin'.

The meal Maw cooks—

Brings funny looks!

Wull Overdid His " New Year," It Seems.

But, Never Mind. Good Night! Sweet Dreams!

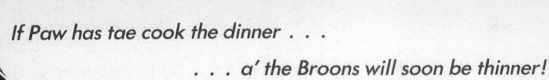

If Paw has tae cook the dinner . . .

. . . a' the Broons will soon be thinner!

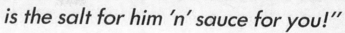

"The train now standing at platform 2 . . .

is the salt for him 'n' sauce for you!"

It's no' up the lum, no' under the chair —

Their haggis has vanished intae thin air!

Here's a " diet "—

Tae keep folk quiet!

Dearie me! It's just no joke —

When the tea goes up in smoke!

Gran'paw's happy Xmas treat—
He packs his things and leaves Glebe St.!

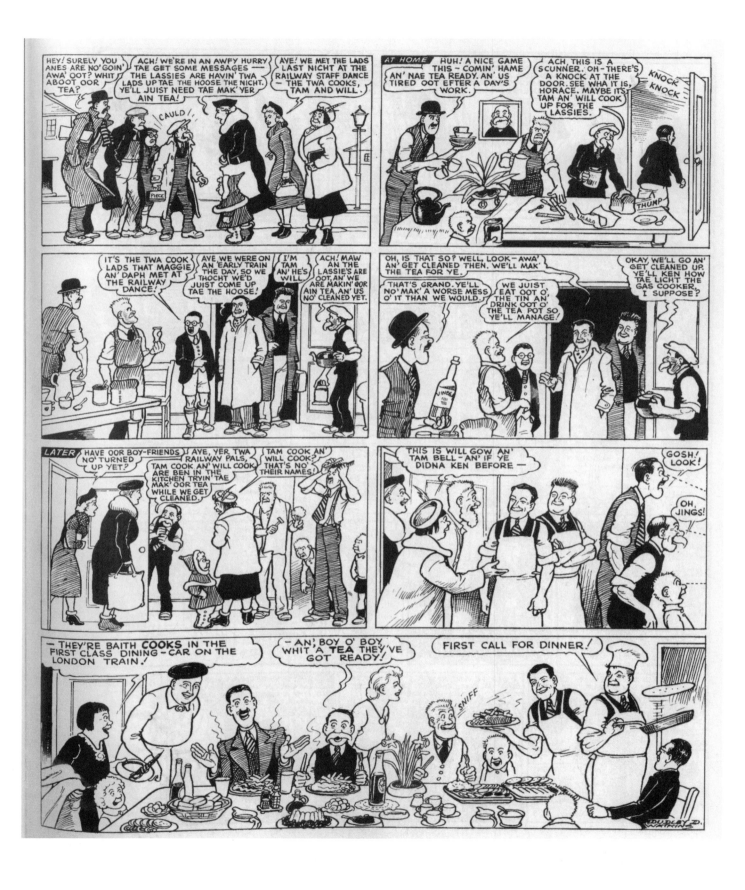

Maggie's meals make Paw Broon wince—

All he wants is tatties and mince!

Wullie has a huge appetite for food in general but the one dish that can bring him back home on time, even when he's catching puddocks, is homemade mince and tatties wi' peas. The perfect pudding to have as afters is Jam Roly-Poly Pudding with custard.

HELPVS
MA
BOABVS

The table's groanin'! Jings, it's braw —

And guess wha's goin' tae scoff it a'!

Wullie Doesna Need To Sulk

He Finds "Good Things In Little Bulk."

By the time the lichts are on . . .

half the birthday cake's gone!

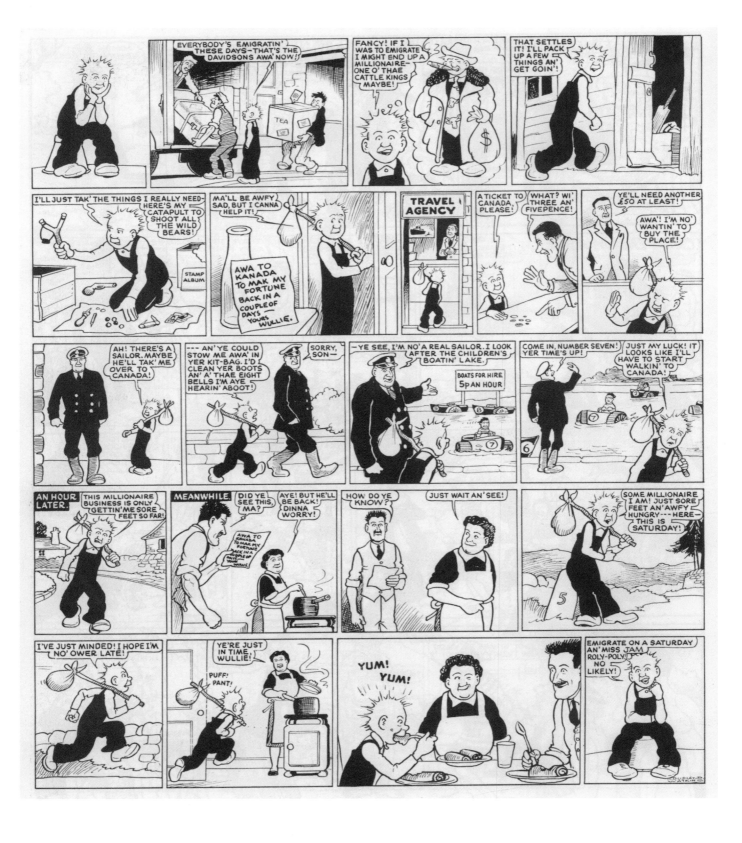

Their Christmas pud—

Is extra good!

The Hairy Hikers

Paw and Granpaw like nothing better than to hike up Glen Bogle and camp wild. Their culinary talent stretches to sausages and beans and a baked potato, cooked in the embers of their fire. Everything tastes better cooked outside, they say.

The Sunday Post

KEN. H. HARRISON.

ON THE HILL THEY'RE A' IN TROUBLE . . .

. . . BUT SUDDENLY, THEY'RE AT THE DOUBLE!

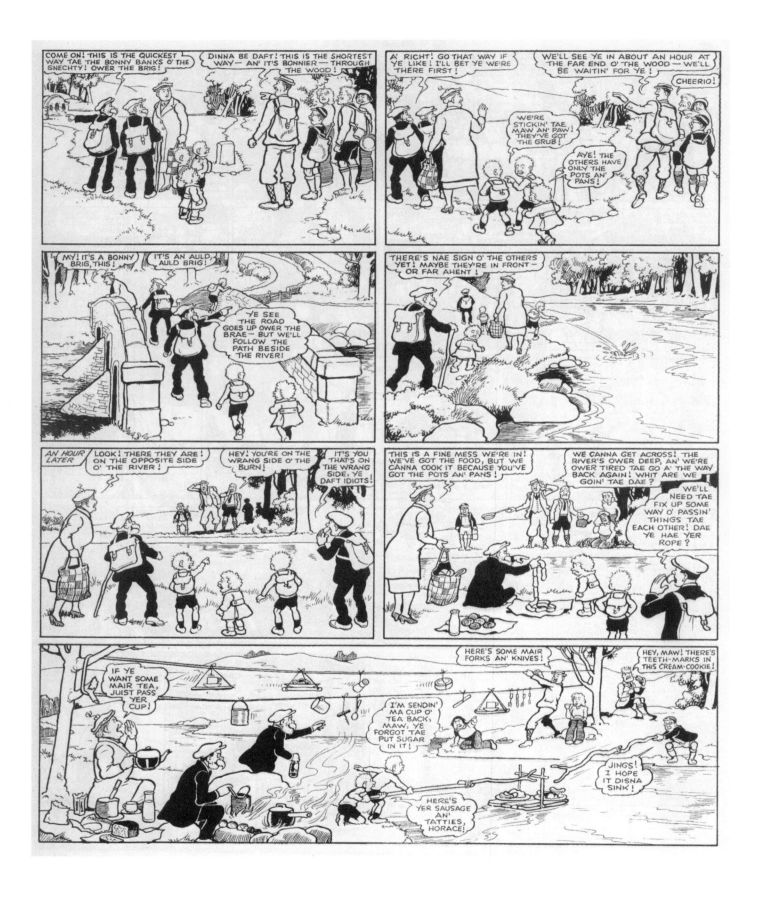

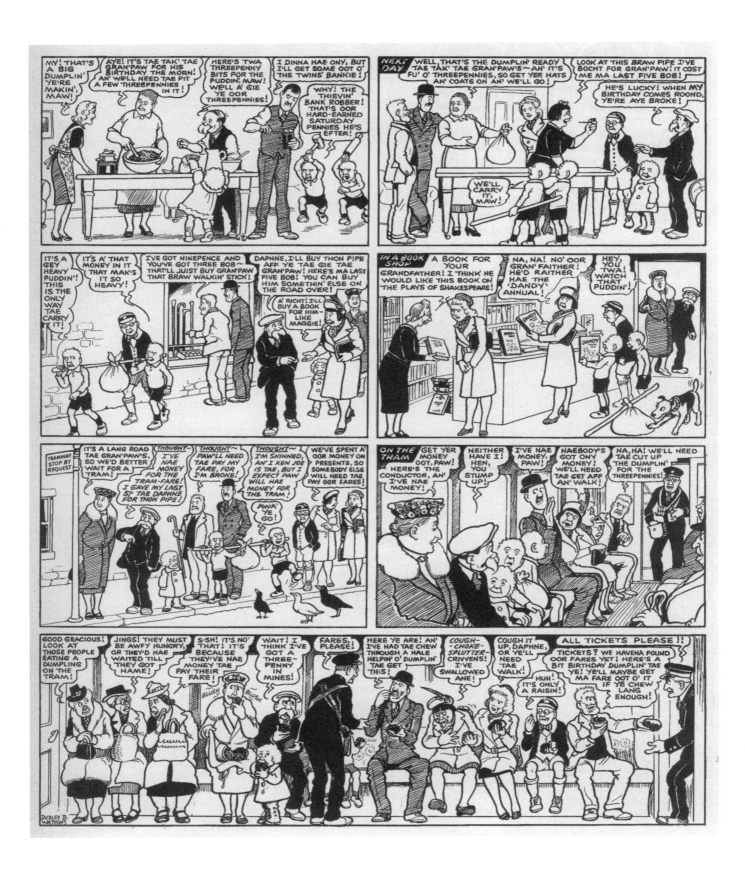

This restaurant is affy posh—

But when Paw treats the folks—oh, gosh!

The price is ower nippy . . .

even at the fish 'n' chippy!

A fish wi' chips 'n' eggs 'n' peas . . .

some invalids are hard tae please!

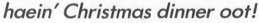

There's lots o' snags aboot . . .

haein' Christmas dinner oot!

A picnic in the open air?

Only if the weather's fair!

What's happenin' the noo?

A soggy barbecue!

TEA IN THE PARK AND NO' INVITED!

PAW DOESNA LIKE TAE BE SAE SLIGHTED!

Ye've tae watch whit ye say . . .

to the Bairn the day!

How's this for meals—

On four big wheels?

Horace is trying to fuse the cuisines of the Orient and Scotland. Paw is hoping he fuses the electrics in the hoose so he stops making such a stink.

Maw's rolling pin has gone missing. Can you find it? There are also 15 hidden neeps to find!

The Bairn knows just who should be—

Tucking in to this daffodil tea!

Here's a big tea-hee —

With Granpaw B!

Wullie's Full Up With Banana.

There's Mair Tae Eat, But Wullie Canna.

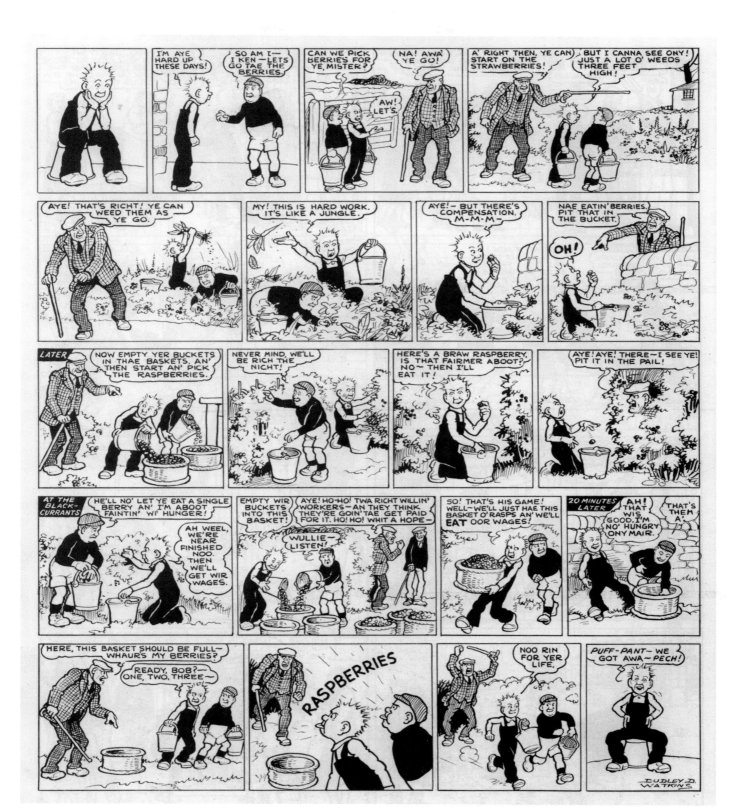

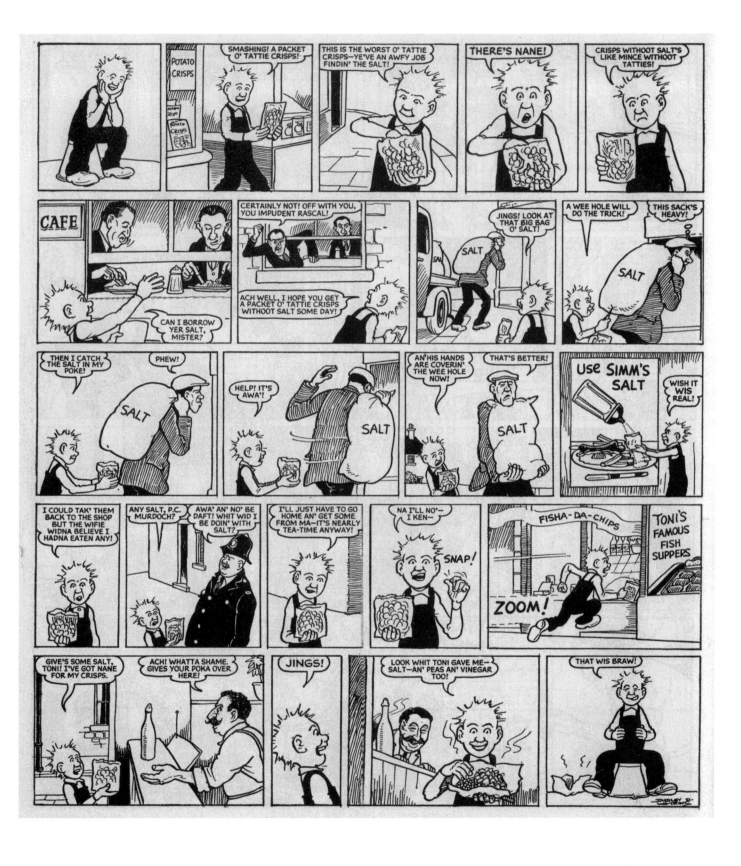

Here's the tale of a key—

It's a real TEA-hee!

The Great Broons Bake Off

Hen Broon had studied hard to be top on the Great Broons Bake Off. The cake had beautifully risen but Daphne was making sure that he was definitely falling!

A colander is missing from the Broon's kitchen. There are 8 of Wee Harry's canine pals to find too!

Tak' a look! Ye're sure tae smile —

This artist's work stands oot a mile!

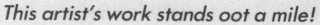

Paw Broon's caught on the hop —

— when he visits the whisky shop.

Maw Broon's signature dish is her famous Clootie Dumpling - a celebration dish that is made for special occasions. Only Maw knows the secret of producing one the size that feeds the eleven braw Broons. On birthdays Maw sometimes puts coins wrapped in paper in the dumpling. The Twins always try to find the slice that would hold the most money.

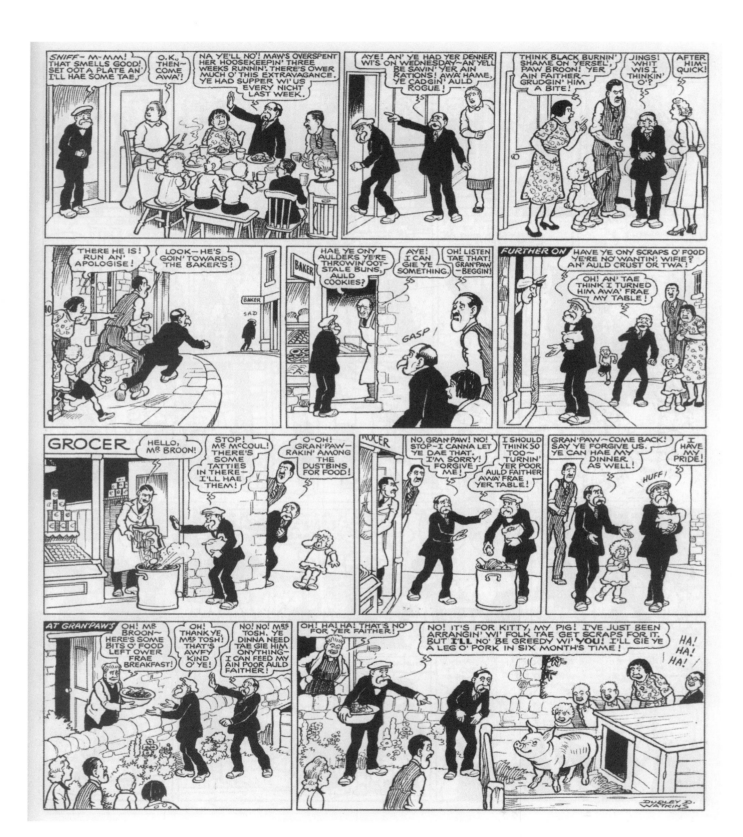

Here's a funny sight! One hungry Broon—

And the best-fed doggie in the toon!

The Broons at tea. As often as not the Broons family, all eleven of them, sat down to eat together. The original of this beautifully drawn scene was on the cover of the 1952 Broons Book.

From master chefs to masters of mischief, The Broons and Oor Wullie have served up a huge helping of happiness over the years. The secret ingredient to their classic family recipe can finally be revealed: a heaped measure of laughter.

Ready, Steady – Sook!

Granpaw Broon, who is the biggest kid, challenges the youngsters to a milkshake race. First to finish wins the prize which Granpaw has arranged – a bag of Granny Sookers, of course.

LOTS O' CAKES AND BISCUITS . . .

AH'LL WIN THE PRIZE FOR THE BIGGEST ONIONS AT THE FLOOER SHOW.

SPECIAL BREW

YOU AYE BEAT TATTIE TAMSON.

SMASHIN'!

M'MM! BRAW! REAL TASTY! NANE O' YER TINNED STUFF THIS, MAW!

ICED LOLLIPOPS 3º EACH

ICED LOLLIPOPS 2º EACH

THAT WIS GRAND! WHIT'S NEXT, MAW? MINCE? STEWIN' STEAK? CHOPS? ROAST BEEF? EH?

SHOVEL!

THAT DID IT!

PEACE AT LAST!

MM!

I DON'T KNOW WHAT FILLING TO PUT IN MY PIE, MAW.

SOMETHING'LL COME TAE YOU, PAUL.

BUY WULLIE'S FAMOUS FRUIT FIZZ 2º A TIME

SUPPER-TIME

YE MAD BOYS BE

THAT WIS BRAW!

ICED LOLLIPOPS 3º EACH

ICED LOLLIPOPS 2º EACH

BRAW! LASHINGS O' BUTTER AN' TREACLE! THIS'LL KEEP ME GOIN' UNTIL TEA-TIME!

M'MM! BRAW! REAL TASTY! NANE O' YER TINNED STUFF THIS, MAW!

PLEASE TAKE A TRAY

I'LL HELP MASEL' TO A CUP AND SAUCER.

JUST TAKE WHIT CAKES YE FANCY, PAW!

WH DID I TEL MARR